A SURVIVOR'S GUIDE TO

THE INVASION OF THE VAMPIRES

BookLife PUBLISHING

©2023
BookLife Publishing Ltd.
King's Lynn, Norfolk
PE30 4LS, UK

Printed in Poland.

A catalogue record for this book is available from the British Library.

ISBN: 978-1-80155-885-3

Written by:
Hermione Redshaw

Edited by:
William Anthony

Designed by:
Drue Rintoul

AN INTRODUCTION TO BOOKLIFE RAPID READERS...

Packed full of gripping topics and twisted tales, BookLife Rapid Readers are perfect for older children looking to propel their reading up to top speed. With three levels based on our planet's fastest animals, children will be able to find the perfect point from which to accelerate their reading journey. From the spooky to the silly, these roaring reads will turn every child at every reading level into a prolific page-turner!

CHEETAH

The fastest animals on land, cheetahs will be taking their first strides as they race to top speed.

MARLIN

The fastest animals under water, marlins will be blasting through their journey.

FALCON

The fastest animals in the air, falcons will be flying at top speed as they tear through the skies.

Photo Credits – Images are courtesy of Shutterstock.com. With thanks to Getty Images, Thinkstock Photo and iStockphoto.
2–3 – Anastacia-azzzya. 4–5 – Lario Tus, Dean Drobot. 6–7 – Virrage Images, Jakub Krechowicz. 8–9 – Independent birds, SB Arts Media. 10–11 – zef art, Ysbrand Cosijn. 12–13 – Ollyy. 14–15 – Nadezhda Bolotina, Adrian Stanica. 16–17 – PeskyMonkey, Claudio Gabriel Gonda. 18–19 – Mark Winfrey, Dm_Cherry. 20–21 – Elenfantasia, Ekaterina Bondaretc. 22–23 – Vera Petruk, Glevalex, Goji. 24–25 – Oleg Golovnev, 3doorsofsun. 26–27 – Maarina Vlasova, Yevhenii Orlov. 28–29 – Albina Tiplyashina, Kiselev Andrey Valerevich. 30 – Denis Makarenko, Anatoliy Karlyuk.

CONTENTS

WORDS THAT LOOK LIKE <u>THIS</u> ARE EXPLAINED IN THE GLOSSARY ON PAGE 31

IT BEGINS...

There are vampires living amongst us right now. There have been for thousands of years.

Vampires are very clever. They can be difficult to spot. They live away from people and do not draw attention to themselves.

Vampires usually hunt two or three times a week. They can survive on animal blood if they need to.

However, drinking only animal blood every day can get boring. A vampire wants a different type of blood. They want human blood!

Vampires mostly live in the countryside. They sneak into towns and villages in search of prey.

Vampires always try to make their hunting look like animal attacks.

Vampires can hunt alone or as part of a larger group.

Are people dying in strange ways? Are the bodies found with bite marks on their necks? Were they drained of blood?

Those bite marks might not have come from animals. They could be vampire attacks!

VAMPIRES IN HISTORY

People have been trying to warn us about vampires for years. Monsters that suck blood have appeared in legends from all around the world.

The monsters look like ordinary men and women. However, they are neither dead nor alive.

The legend of Brahmaparusha is famous in India.

In some stories, Brahmaparusha hangs upside down from trees, like a bat.

It drains the blood of its victims into a human skull. It then uses the skull as a cup to drink from.

Vrykolakas are evil creatures from Greek legends. They drink so much blood that their skin turns red.

Vrykolakas leave their graves to visit nearby towns. If you open your door when a vrykolakas knocks, you are sure to die.

One of the most famous vampires is Count Dracula from Transylvania. Dracula is very old and clever. He can turn into a bat, a wolf and smoke.

Dracula has no shadow or reflection. He also has two sharp fangs.

SPOTTING A VAMPIRE

Recognising the signs of a vampire is an important skill. You will need it to become a vampire slayer. There can be no mistakes when the vampire invasion begins.

CLOTHING

Some vampires wear what they died in. Their clothes could be very old. You might spot a vampire wearing a cape.

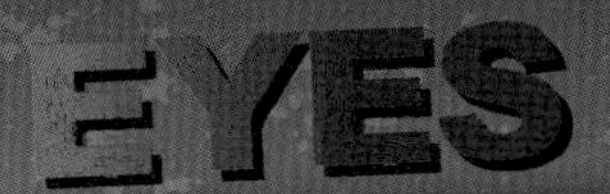

EYES

Vampires' eyes glow red when they smell blood.

FANGS

Vampires have long, sharp fangs.

SKIN

Vampires have cold skin.

PLACES TO AVOID

The best way to avoid a vampire attack is to keep out of their way. Stay as far away as possible from their homes.

Be careful!

Vampires usually move into abandoned castles. The castles may still look empty after a vampire has moved in.

Vampires can live anywhere in the world. However, Dracula and many other vampires come from Transylvania.

Transylvania is an area in the European country of Romania. Hundreds of years ago, Romanian vampires built lots of castles high up in the Carpathian mountains.

Some vampires stay in graveyards. They stay in a coffin deep below ground to avoid the Sun during the day.

Be careful walking through a graveyard in the dark. Graveyards are only safe to visit during the daytime.

Vampires can travel far when they turn into bats. However, they need to rest during the day.

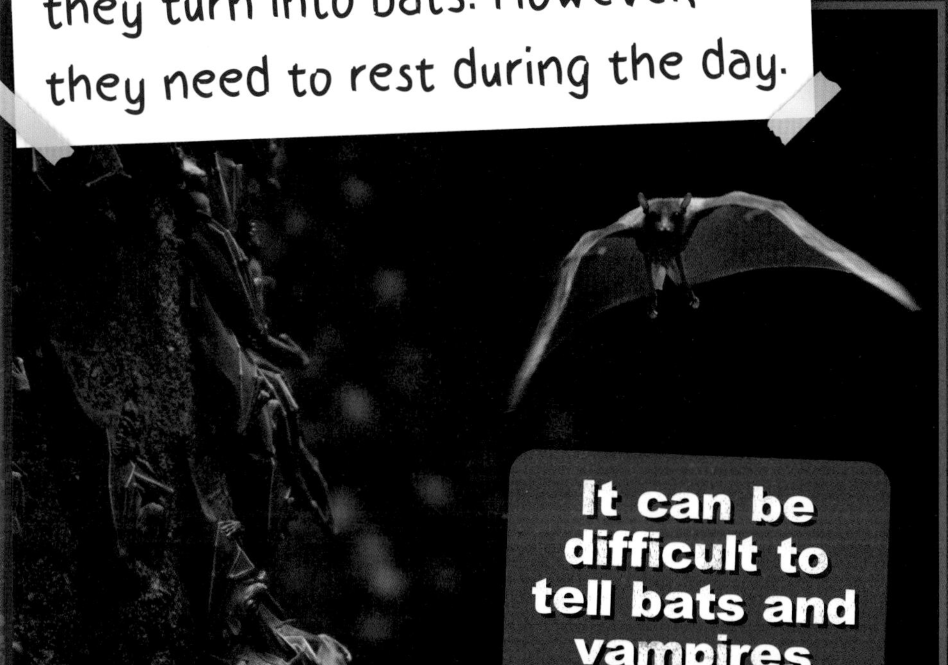

It can be difficult to tell bats and vampires apart.

You might find vampires hanging upside down in caves.

HIDEOUT HUNTING

You will need a base where you can safely hide. You might need to be there for a long time.

Your hideout should be far away from castles, caves and graveyards. The best hideouts get lots of sunlight.

Make sure your hideout is stocked up on food, water and weapons. Then, lock all the doors and windows.

Vampires do not have reflections. Place a mirror near your entrance. You will be able to check if anyone visiting is secretly a vampire.

WEAPONS AND TOOLS

Vampires could turn up where you least expect them. You need to be prepared.

Having the right weapons could mean the difference between life and death. The best weapons are small, light and easily hidden.

GARLIC

Vampire slayers throughout history have used garlic to keep vampires away. No vampire will want to come anywhere near you while you stink of garlic.

Wear a string of garlic cloves around your neck while you get your weapons ready.

HOLY OBJECTS

Vampires do not like holy objects, such as the Bible, crucifixes and holy water.

Try carrying some of these around with you. You can open your Bible and start reading from the first page you come across if you see a vampire.

WOODEN STAKE

Vampires cannot be killed easily. They are incredibly strong and can heal quickly.

The easiest way to kill a vampire is a wooden stake through the heart. The stake can be made of any wood that has a sharp, pointy end.

DEFENDING YOURSELF

Your hideout should be strong enough to keep you safe for a while. However, you may have to head outside when your supplies begin to run low.

Always go out in a group. Take plenty of wooden stakes with you.

Try to make sure that you are out in the sunlight. It is very important that you only ever go out during the daytime.

Move out of shadows as soon as possible. Any vampires that follow you will burst into flames and die.

You could try to trick a vampire to follow you into the sunlight.

Try reading from your Bible in a loud, clear voice. This should stall the vampire enough that it might not notice where it's going.

Most vampires are too clever to be tricked. You will have to brave the shadows.

Grab your wooden stake. You will need to get close enough to reach the vampire's heart. Hold your crucifix in your free hand.

LIVING IN THE VAMPIRE INVASION

You will need to wait out the invasion from the safety of your hideout. It won't end overnight. Unless you go out and fight every vampire one by one, of course.

Sit back and settle down. It's going to be a long few months...

The vampires may start to become desperate towards the end of the invasion.

They will start running out of humans. This will make them very hungry. They might risk coming out in the Sun to launch an attack.

SURVIVING THE VAMPIRE INVASION

You have nothing to worry about if you follow this guide.

Keep your doors are locked. Top up your garlic supply whenever you head outside. Most importantly, make sure you are back in your hideout before sunset.

GLOSSARY

abandoned left without an owner

base hideout

cloves a section of garlic

crucifixes images or models of a cross that are important in some religions

desperate very sad and upset because of having little or no hope

holy connected to a religion

legends stories from the past that many people believe but cannot be proven are true

prey animals, or people, that are hunted for food

reflection an image that is seen in a mirror or on a shiny surface

stake a stick with a sharp, pointed end

INDEX